Welcome

It
to
an

The One Day
Creative Retreat
ACTIVITY BOOK

There is a Monastic tradition of splitting
the day into sections known as the canonical
hours. Most commonly these are known as:
Invitatory, the introduction to the theme and
focus for the day; Matins; Lauds; Terce; Sext;
None; Vespers and Compline.

We have split this day retreat into eight
sections but please don't feel you have to do
all of the sections in one day, you could plan
to have a retreat starting on one evening
and run into the next day or stretch it over
a weekend. Start with the Invitatory section
and focus activity and then work through
each section at your own pace.

Finally, don't undo any good by worrying that
you haven't completed everything. Please look
at the comments at the back of this book for
some additional thoughts and ideas.

With every blessing,

Mark and Mary Fleeson
Holy Island

Invitatory
An invitation.

Today is a day when usual things are pushed
aside, a day for reflection and restoration,
for quiet and prayer. A day for you and God
to spend quality time together.

Give this day to God.

Creator God, I give this time to You,
I welcome You into this place
And into my life.
Speak clearly and teach me to listen.

Creator God, I give my concerns to You,
I lay my burdens at Your feet,
Help me to leave them there.

On the opposite page is a 'focus' activity,
colouring. For a while leave behind your busy
thoughts, your everyday concerns and just focus
on the rhythm of shading. If you said the prayer
above then you have already invited God to be
with you, enjoy being in the loving presence
of your Creator.

THIS DAY IS YOURS MY GOD

Mattins
Morning Prayer

Today we are looking at Psalm 51, 10-12 which reads:

Create a pure heart in me, O God, and put a new and loyal spirit in me. Do not banish me from Your presence; do not take Your Holy Spirit away from me. Give me again the joy that comes from Your salvation, and make me willing to obey You. (GNT)

Sit somewhere quiet and consider the words of the Psalm above. Think of it as a prayer.

What could happen if we prayed the words of the Psalm everyday?

Write your reflections here or in a notebook.

From your reflections pick three words that summarise the words of the Psalm to you and write them inside the Trinity knot opposite.

Trace the knot with your finger and ask for more insight to be revealed to you.

Lauds
The second monastic hour.

Create a pure heart in me, O God, and
put a new and loyal spirit in me.

God wants to give us the opportunity
to start afresh, whatever we have done,
or left undone.
Today we can be made as new.
It is never too late to change.

What changes do you think God wants you
to make today?

Write down your reflections.

Terce
The third monastic hour.

Do not banish me from Your presence; do not take Your Holy Spirit away from me.

Jesus said,
"If you love me, keep my commands. And I will ask the Father, and He will give you another advocate to help you and be with you forever, the Spirit of truth." John 14:15-17

Many times it is us who banish God from our presence and although the Holy Spirit doesn't leave we are very capable of ignoring that 'still, small voice'.

Days like today are ideal opportunities to listen to God. On the next page is a spiral finger labyrinth to help you focus. Trace the spiral slowly, as you head towards the centre try to leave your awareness of the sounds around you and the bubbling thoughts in your head behind so that when you reach the middle you are better able to hear God. When you make your way back out try to listen for that 'still, small voice.'

Sext
The sixth monastic hour.

Sext, or Sixth Hour, is a fixed time of prayer of the Divine Office of almost all the traditional Christian liturgies. It consists mainly of psalms and is said at noon. Its name comes from Latin and refers to the sixth hour of the day after dawn.

Give me again the joy that comes from Your salvation, and make me willing to obey You.

The deep joy that comes from salvation isn't often the sort that has you grinning from ear to ear and giggling at nothing, instead it is more of a sense of purpose and quiet confidence. It is that confidence as a loved and lovable child of God that helps us to willingly obey when we are called.

This is what the Sovereign Lord, the Holy One of Israel, says: "Only in returning to me and resting in me will you be saved. In quietness and confidence is your strength."
Isaiah 30:15 (NLT)

When do you feel, or when have you felt most confident that you are a beloved child of God? Do you think that you can create situations that help you feel closer to God?

None
The ninth monastic hour.

None or the Ninth Hour is said around 3 p.m. Its name comes from Latin and refers to the ninth hour of the day after dawn.

The Lord your God is in your midst, a mighty one who will save; He will rejoice over you with gladness; He will quiet you by His love; He will exult over you with loud singing. Zephaniah 3:17 (ESV)

Write a short invitation prayer to use when you want to welcome God into a situation or use the prayer below.

Thank you for this moment,
May it be sacred,
O God,
make it Yours,

Thank you for this life,
May I be ready,
O God,
make me Yours,

Thank you for this voice,
May it be prayer,
O God,
make it Yours.

A good starting point for writing a prayer is the ACTS acrostic...

Adoration - love God

Confession - sorry God

Thanksgiving - thank God

Supplication - ask God

Vespers
Evening prayer.

Vespers is the sunset evening prayer service.

"Remember not the former things, nor consider the things of old. Behold, I am doing a new thing; now it springs forth, do you not perceive it? I will make a way in the wilderness and rivers in the desert."
Isaiah 43:18-19 (ESV)

As sunset marks the end of a period of time that will never be repeated so a quiet day may become a transition day, a time of moving from old ways and understandings into a new place. The experiences of the past will never happen again, we can choose whether to learn from them and move on or dwell on them and prevent ourselves from greeting the future with a fresh vision and a clean heart.

When your retreat is over will there still be memories that hold you back, ones that prevent you from fully surrendering to Gods plan for you?

Opposite is a blank page, are you that page?

Compline
The final monastic service of the day.

The English word Compline is derived from the Latin completorium, as Compline is the completion of the working day.

Before you return to your everyday life, a prayer...

Circle me Creator God,
Keep Your protection around me,
Let Your love shine from me.

Circle me Saviour Jesus,
Keep Your example before me,
Let Your hope fill my being.

Circle me Guiding Spirit
Keep Your mercy within me,
Let Your forgiveness restore me.

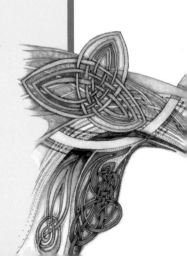

On the opposite page is another colouring outline. At the close of your retreat use it to help you clarify what God has been saying to you. It may be helpful to write words in the spaces rather than shade all over.